USBORNE
ANIMAL
STICKER ATLAS

Ruth Brocklehurst
Designed by Michelle Lawrence
Cartographer: Craig Asquith

Edited by Stephanie Turnbull
Natural history consultant: Margaret Rostron

Contents

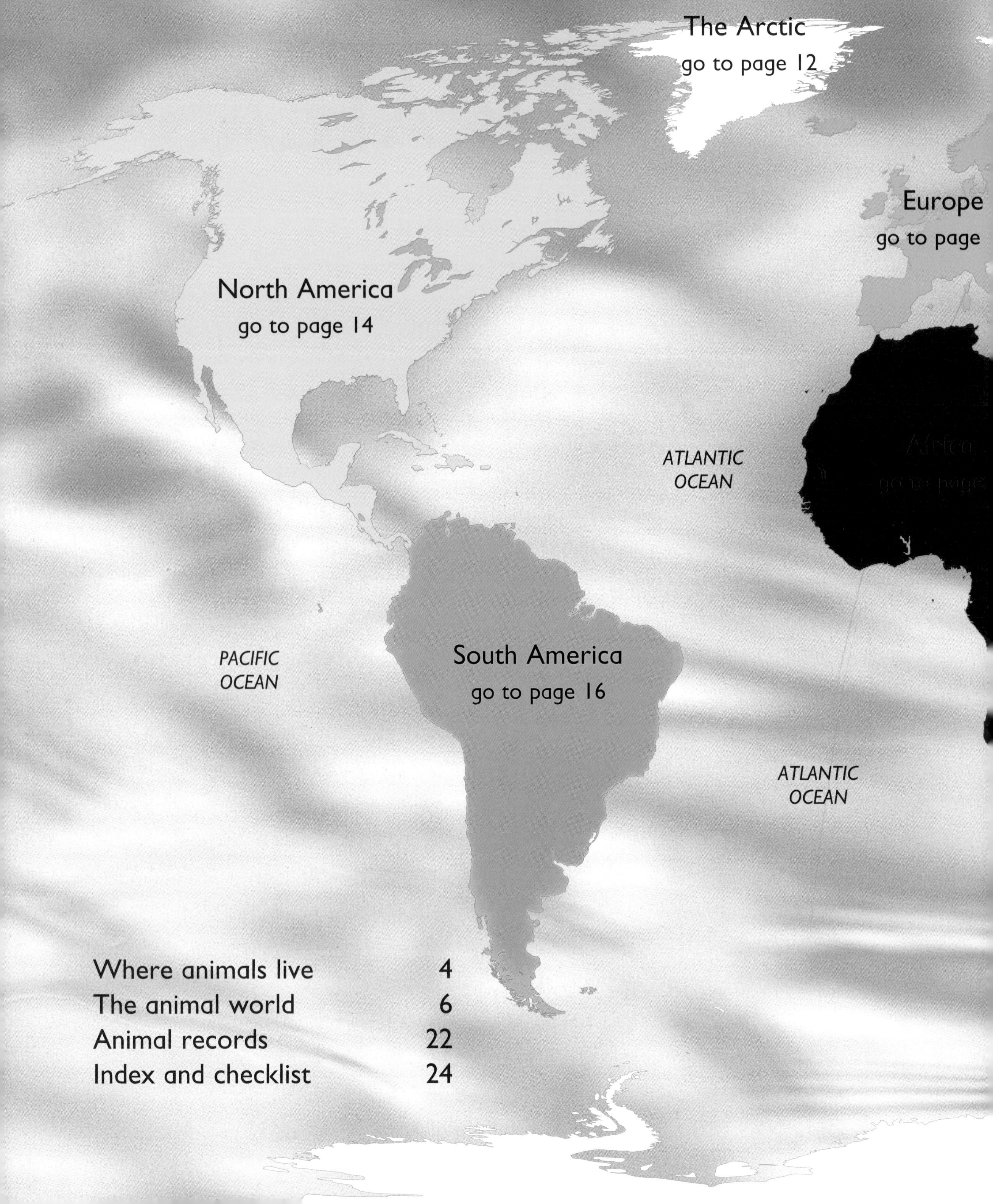

ARCTIC OCEAN

The Arctic
go to page 12

Europe
go to page

North America
go to page 14

ATLANTIC
OCEAN

Africa
go to page

PACIFIC
OCEAN

South America
go to page 16

ATLANTIC
OCEAN

ARCTIC OCEAN

Internet link

For a link to a website where you can see
photographs of animals from around the world,
and read about how they live in the wild, go to
www.usborne-quicklinks.com and follow the
instructions there.

Asia
go to page 20

PACIFIC
OCEAN

INDIAN
OCEAN

Australasia
and Oceania
go to page 18

SOUTHERN OCEAN

Antarctica
go to page 13

Where animals live

The maps in this book show where animals live around the world. Animals live in all kinds of places, from dusty deserts to leafy rainforests. Here are some of the main places.

This is a tree frog from the Amazon Rainforest in South America.

Grasslands

Grasslands are open places where grasses grow and there aren't many trees.

■ **Green grassland** – In mild, rainy places, the grasslands are lush and green.

■ **Hot grassland** – In hot places, such as Africa, there is a long, dry season when the grass grows dry and golden.

Many grassland animals, such as these zebras and antelopes, eat grass and live in groups called herds.

Forests

Forest are places that are full of trees. They vary depending on the weather.

■ **Tropical rainforests** – Rainforests grow where it is hot and rainy all year. They are steamy places with huge, tall trees.

■ **Deciduous forests** – Deciduous trees lose their leaves every winter and grow new ones in the spring. They grow in places where summers are warm and winters are cool.

■ **Coniferous forests** – In cold parts of the world, there are forests of conifer trees, which stay green all year round.

Penguins live near the South Pole. Chicks huddle close to their parents, so they don't get cold.

Hot and cold places

It is difficult for animals to live where it is very hot and dry or freezing cold.

■ **Ice and snow** – The North and South Poles are the coldest places in the world. They are frozen all year round.

■ **Tundra** – Near the poles is bare, partly frozen land called tundra. Winters there are long and dark, so plants only grow in the summer.

■ **Mountains** – The higher up a mountain you go, the colder and windier it is. The highest peaks are often covered in snow.

■ **Deserts** – Deserts are very dry places with hardly any plants. Animals there have to survive extremely hot days and very cold nights.

How to use this book

There are over 200 animal stickers in this book. To find out where each animal comes from, try to match the stickers to the black and white drawings on the maps.

The stickers are numbered, so you can tell which map they go on. A list on each map tells you the names of the animals, and there's a checklist at the back of the book to help you.

Using the key

The shading on the maps shows what the land is like in different places. This key explains what the shading and the lines on the maps represent.

■ Forests	☐ Other (grassland, farmland and cities)
☐ Deserts	
■ Mountains	■ Seas and oceans
☐ Tundra	∫ Country boundaries
☐ Ice and snow	⸾ Country boundaries through water
∫ Rivers	

World map

Every map in this book has a small world map next to it. The shaded area shows you which part of the world is shown on the big map.

This is the world map that goes with the big map of South America.

The animal world

There are millions of different animals around the world, but they all belong to large groups. Here you can find out about the different groups of animals.

Many birds, such as this parakeet, have bright feathers and beaks.

Mammals

There are many different types of mammals, including humans, whales, cats, dogs, bats and monkeys.

- **Milk** – Mammals look after their babies and feed them with milk.

- **Hair** – Most mammals have fur or hair.

- **Backbones** – All mammals have backbones. Almost all mammals have seven bones in their neck. This includes the tallest giraffes and the smallest mice.

Leopards belong to the cat group of mammals.

Birds

Birds are the only animals that have feathers.

- **Eggs** – Female birds lay eggs. They sit on the eggs to keep them warm until the chicks hatch out.

- **Nests** – Most birds build nests to protect their young.

- **Wings** – All birds have wings but some, such as emus and penguins, can't fly.

Creepy-crawlies

Creepy-crawlies make up the largest animal group in the world. They include insects, spiders and bugs.

- **Insects** – Insects include ants, bees and butterflies. All insects have bodies that are made up of three sections. They have six legs and most have wings.

- **Legs** – Spiders and scorpions have eight legs. Millipedes have up to 700 legs – that's more than any other animal.

This is a huntsman spider, from Australia.

Reptiles

Snakes, lizards, turtles and crocodiles are all examples of reptiles.

■ **Cold-blooded** – Reptiles are cold-blooded. This means that their body temperature depends on their surroundings.

■ **Scales** – Scaly skin protects reptiles from drying up in the sun.

■ **Eggs** – Most reptiles lay leathery eggs, which are left to hatch on their own.

This reptile is a chameleon. It can change the pattern of its skin to blend with its surroundings.

Poisonous slime oozes out of this South American frog's skin.

Amphibians

Amphibians include frogs, toads and newts.

■ **Eggs** – Most amphibians hatch from eggs, which are kept moist or laid in water.

■ **Water and land** – The young live in water and the adults usually live on land.

■ **Breathing** – Amphibians can breathe through their skin, which is smooth and moist.

Water animals

Many animals live in lakes, rivers and seas. As well as millions of fish, these include animals such as lobsters and squid, and some mammals.

■ **Inside out** – Lobsters, crabs and shrimps have hard outer skeletons, but no bones inside their bodies.

■ **Soft bodies** – Jellyfish and sea anemones have soft, hollow bodies and stinging tentacles.

Many fish, like these, swim in large groups called schools or shoals.

Africa

ATLANTIC
OCEAN

Madeira

Canary
Islands

MOROCCO

TUNISIA

ALGERIA

LIE

1

WESTERN
SAHARA

MAURITANIA

MALI

NIGER

CAPE VERDE

SENEGAL

THE GAMBIA

GUINEA-BISSAU

GUINEA

SIERRA
LEONE

LIBERIA

IVORY
COAST

GHANA

BURKINA
FASO

NIGERIA

CH

4

BENIN

TOGO

CAMEROON

EQUATORIAL
GUINEA

SAO TOME
AND PRINCIPE

GABON

ATLANTIC
OCEAN

CONGO

8

13

ANGO

NAMIB

Mediterranean Sea

EGYPT

Red Sea

SUDAN

ERITREA

DJIBOUTI

ETHIOPIA

NTRAL
RICAN
UBLIC

DEMOCRATIC
PUBLIC OF CONGO

KENYA

SOMALIA

INDIAN OCEAN

18

UGANDA

RWANDA

BURUNDI

26

TANZANIA

COMOROS

ZAMBIA

MALAWI

MOZAMBIQUE

ZIMBABWE

TSWANA

21

MAURITIUS

MADAGASCAR

SWAZILAND

LESOTHO

OUTH
FRICA

African
animals

1	Dolphin
2	Frigate bird
3	Ground squirrel
4	Pangolin
5	Viper
6	Camel
7	Chimpanzee
8	Great white shark
9	Scorpion
10	Hippopotamus
11	Gorilla
12	African parrot
13	Springbok
14	Meerkat
15	Fennec fox
16	Crocodile
17	Rhinoceros
18	African elephant
19	Cheetah
20	Giraffes
21	Ostrich
22	Baboons
23	Zebras
24	Lion
25	Hammerhead shark
26	Butterfly fish
27	Ring-tailed lemur

The numbers in the key
are on the stickers.

Europe

ICELAND

132

European animals

28   Puffin
29   Blue whale
30   Red fox
31   Hedgehog
32   Mole
33   Humpback whale
34   Kingfisher
35   Flamingo
36   Bee-eater
37   Octopus
38   Killer whale
39   Reindeer
40   Pig
41   Hare
42   Red squirrel
43   Field mouse
44   Barn owl
45   European bison
46   Fallow deer
47   Arctic hare
48   Lynx
49   Beaver
50   Wild boar
51   Blue tit
52   Common toad
53   Spoonbill
54   Short-eared owl
55   Golden eagle
56   Black stork
57   Siberian chipmunk

The numbers in the key
are on the stickers.

10

ATLANTIC OCEAN

Shetland
Islands

Orkney
Islands

NORWAY

40

North
Sea

DENMARK

UNITED
KINGDOM

IRELAND

NETHERLANDS

BELGIUM

GERMANY

LUXEMBOURG

FRANCE

AUST

SWITZERLAND

Bay of
Biscay

SLOVE

MONACO

PORTUGAL

ANDORRA

Corsica

ITA

SPAIN

Sardinia

37

Mediterranean Sea

Sicily

MALT

WEDEN

FINLAND

RUSSIA

47

Barents Sea

ESTONIA

LATVIA

Baltic Sea

LITHUANIA

BELARUS

POLAND

UKRAINE

ZECH PUBLIC

LOVAKIA

MOLDOVA

Caspian Sea

UNGARY

ROATIA

OSNIA AND ERZEGOVINA

ROMANIA

Black Sea

BULGARIA

MACEDONIA

ALBANIA

GREECE

Aegean Sea

TURKEY

ERBIA AND ONTENEGRO

Crete

CYPRUS

11

The Arctic

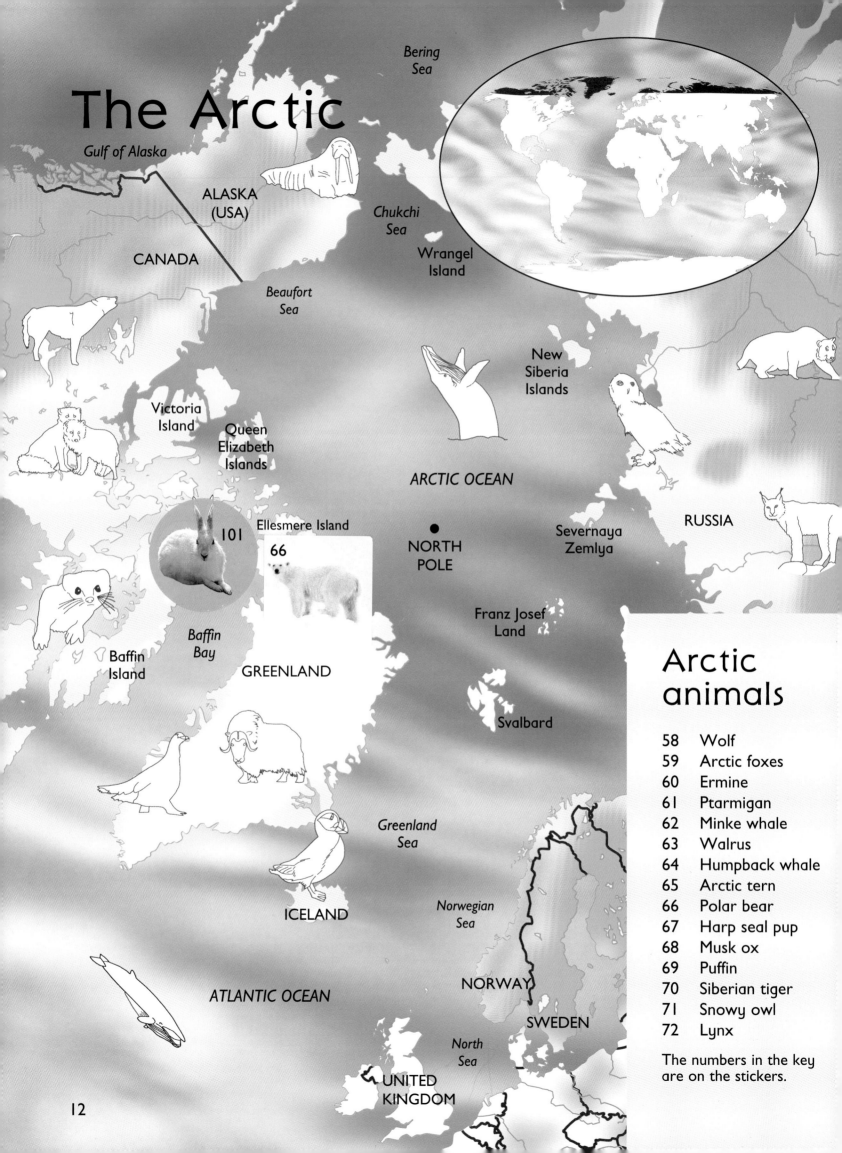

Bering Sea

Gulf of Alaska

ALASKA (USA)

Chukchi Sea

Wrangel Island

CANADA

Beaufort Sea

New Siberia Islands

ARCTIC OCEAN

Victoria Island

Queen Elizabeth Islands

RUSSIA

Ellesmere Island

101

66

NORTH POLE

Severnaya Zemlya

Baffin Bay

GREENLAND

Franz Josef Land

Baffin Island

Svalbard

Greenland Sea

ICELAND

Norwegian Sea

NORWAY

ATLANTIC OCEAN

SWEDEN

North Sea

UNITED KINGDOM

Arctic animals

58 Wolf
59 Arctic foxes
60 Ermine
61 Ptarmigan
62 Minke whale
63 Walrus
64 Humpback whale
65 Arctic tern
66 Polar bear
67 Harp seal pup
68 Musk ox
69 Puffin
70 Siberian tiger
71 Snowy owl
72 Lynx

The numbers in the key are on the stickers.

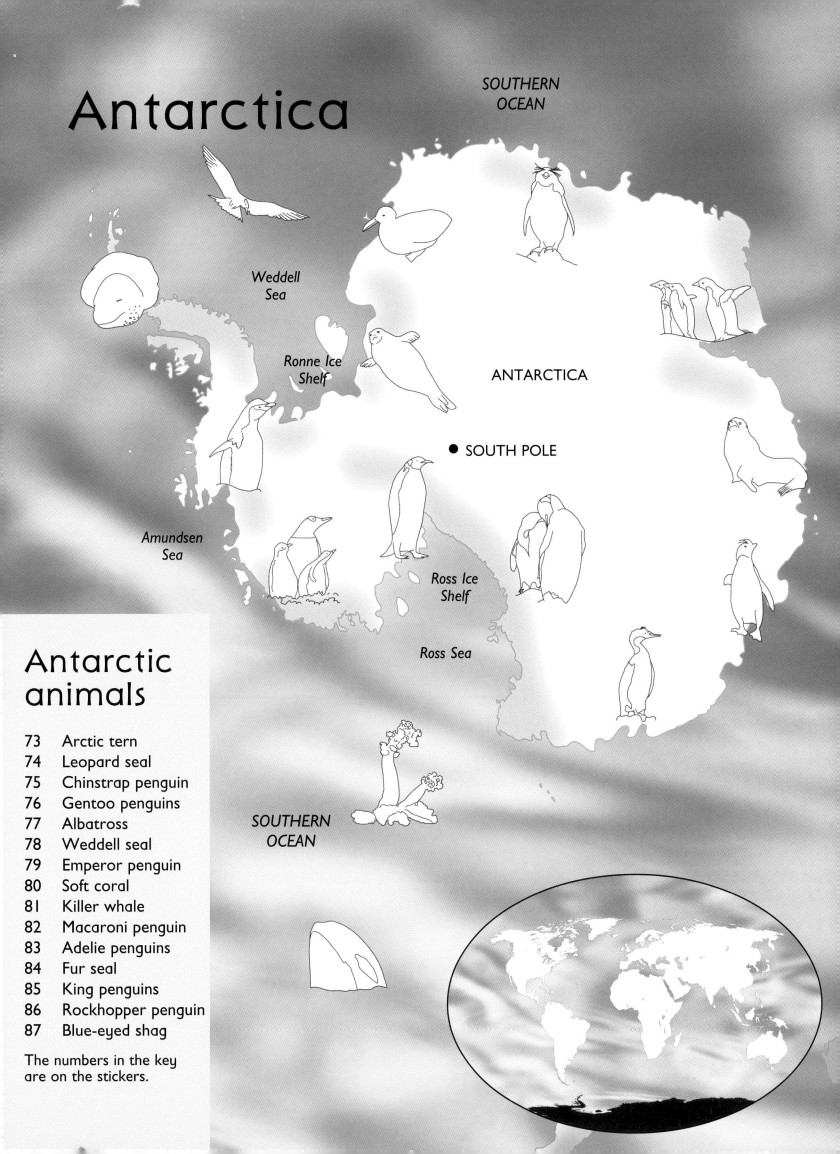

Antarctica

SOUTHERN OCEAN

Weddell Sea

Ronne Ice Shelf

ANTARCTICA

● SOUTH POLE

Amundsen Sea

Ross Ice Shelf

Ross Sea

SOUTHERN OCEAN

Antarctic animals

The numbers in the key are on the stickers.

North America

GREENLAND

ATLANTIC
OCEAN

Labrador
Sea

Baffin
Bay

Ellesmere
Island

Queen Elizabeth
Islands

Baffin
Island

Hudson
Bay

Victoria
Island

The Great

Beaufort
Sea

CANADA

ALASKA
(USA)

Gulf of
Alaska

PACIFIC
OCEAN

North American animals

88 Polar bear
89 Bald eagle
90 Killer whale
91 Bobcat
92 Coyote
93 Raccoon
94 Bighorn sheep
95 Gila monster
96 Rattlesnake
97 Elephant seal
98 Great white shark
99 Red-kneed tarantula
100 Monarch butterfly
101 Arctic hare
102 Grizzly bear
103 Moose
104 Wolf
105 Buffalo
106 Skunk
107 Alligator
108 Cuban tree frog
109 Kinkajou
110 Arctic foxes
111 Ptarmigen
112 Snowy owl
113 Beaver
114 Blue jay
115 Humpback whale
116 Canada goose
117 Puffin

The numbers in the key are on the stickers.

UNITED STATES OF AMERICA (USA)

MEXICO

Gulf of Mexico

THE BAHAMAS

CUBA

JAMAICA

Caribbean Sea

BELIZE

GUATEMALA

EL SALVADOR

HONDURAS

NICARAGUA

COSTA RICA

PANAMA

Galapagos Islands

PACIFIC OCEAN

163

South America

ATLANTIC
OCEAN

VENEZUELA

GUYANA

SURINAM

FRENCH
GUIANA

COLOMBIA

BRAZIL

ECUADOR

PERU

BOLIVIA

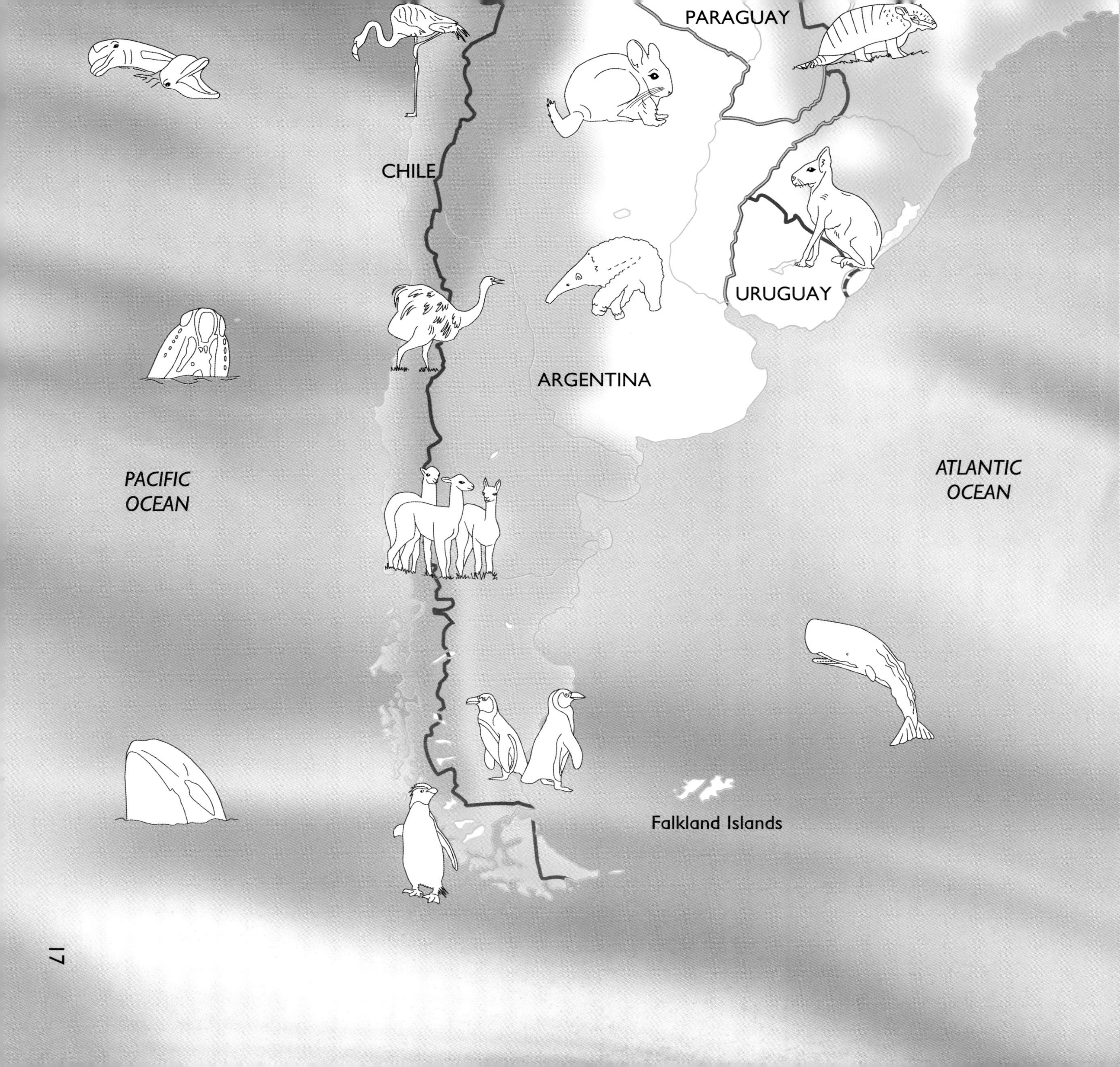

South American animals

118 Puma
119 Peccary
120 Jaguar
121 Condor
122 Spider monkey
123 Llama
124 Dolphins
125 Right whale
126 Giant tree frog
127 Spectacled bear
128 Flamingo
129 Rhea
130 Guanacos
131 Magellan penguins
132 Killer whale
133 Rockhopper penguin
134 Scarlet ibis
135 Caiman
136 Sloth
137 Small blue macaw
138 Toucan
139 Morpho butterfly
140 Chinchilla
141 Giant anteater
142 Green turtle
143 Capybara
144 Anaconda
145 Golden lion tamarin
146 Armadillo
147 Mara
148 Sperm whale

The numbers in the key are on the stickers.

PARAGUAY

URUGUAY

CHILE

ARGENTINA

ATLANTIC OCEAN

PACIFIC OCEAN

Falkland Islands

17

Australasia and Oceania

Northern Mariana Islands

PALAU

FEDERATED STATES OF MICRONESIA

PAPUA NEW GUINEA

New Guinea

SOLOMON ISLANDS

Arafura Sea

Timor Sea

Great Barrier Reef

AUSTRALIA

INDIAN OCEAN

98

Tasmania

18

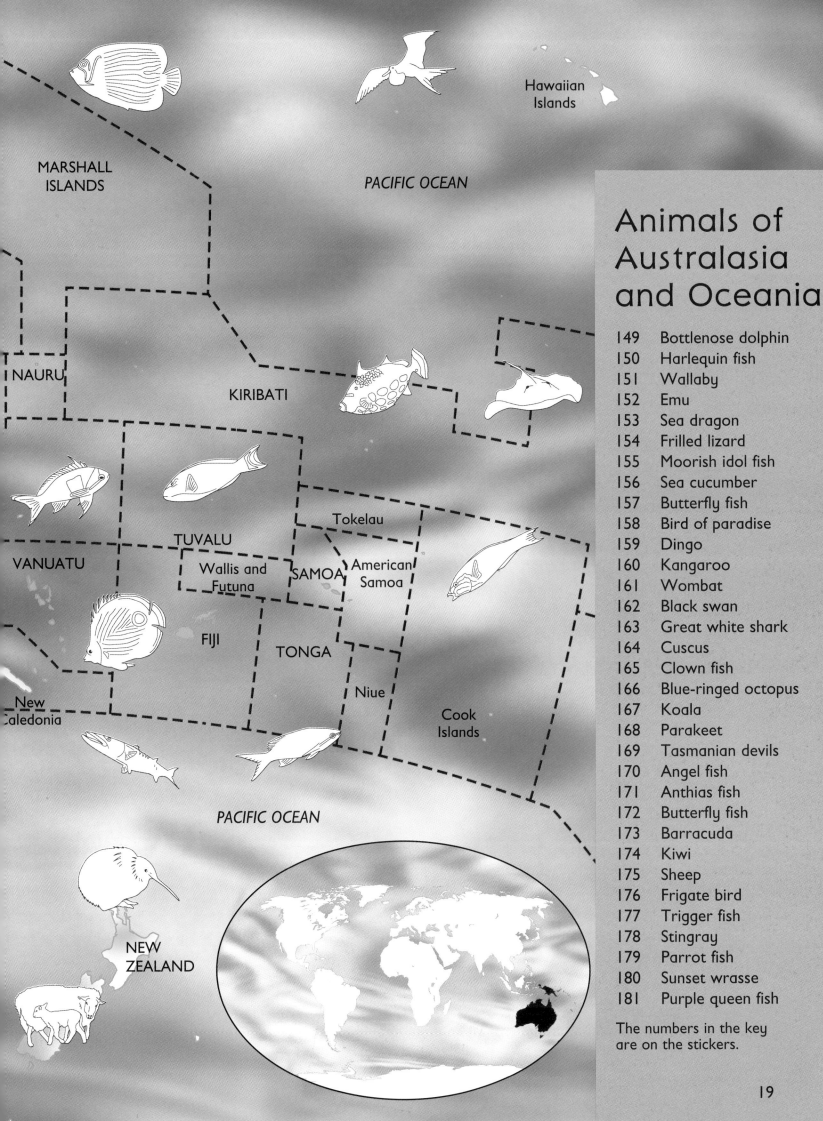

MARSHALL
ISLANDS

PACIFIC OCEAN

Hawaiian
Islands

NAURU

KIRIBATI

TUVALU

VANUATU

Wallis and
Futuna

SAMOA

Tokelau

American
Samoa

FIJI

TONGA

Niue

Cook
Islands

New
Caledonia

PACIFIC OCEAN

NEW
ZEALAND

Animals of Australasia and Oceania

149   Bottlenose dolphin
150   Harlequin fish
151   Wallaby
152   Emu
153   Sea dragon
154   Frilled lizard
155   Moorish idol fish
156   Sea cucumber
157   Butterfly fish
158   Bird of paradise
159   Dingo
160   Kangaroo
161   Wombat
162   Black swan
163   Great white shark
164   Cuscus
165   Clown fish
166   Blue-ringed octopus
167   Koala
168   Parakeet
169   Tasmanian devils
170   Angel fish
171   Anthias fish
172   Butterfly fish
173   Barracuda
174   Kiwi
175   Sheep
176   Frigate bird
177   Trigger fish
178   Stingray
179   Parrot fish
180   Sunset wrasse
181   Purple queen fish

The numbers in the key
are on the stickers.

Asia

ARCTIC OCEAN

RUSSIA

KAZAKHSTAN

Black Sea

GEORGIA

TURKEY

ARMENIA

AZERBAIJAN

UZBEKISTAN

KYRGYZSTAN

CHINA

Mediterranean Sea

Cyprus

SYRIA

TURKMENISTAN

TAJIKISTAN

LEBANON

IRAN

ISRAEL

IRAQ

AFGHANISTAN

JORDAN

KUWAIT

PAKISTAN

SAUDI ARABIA

QATAR

NEPAL

BHUTAN

UNITED ARAB EMIRATES

BANGLADESH

INDIA

BURMA (MYANMAR)

OMAN

Red Sea

Arabian Sea

LA

Bay of Bengal

THAILAN

YEMEN

Socotra

SRI LANKA

MALDIVES

INDIAN OCEAN

Sumatra

20

Bering Sea

Sea of Okhotsk

MONGOLIA

NORTH KOREA

SOUTH KOREA

JAPAN

East China Sea

TAIWAN

South China Sea

PHILIPPINES

CAMBODIA

VIETNAM

Philippine Sea

PACIFIC OCEAN

BRUNEI

MALAYSIA

Borneo

Celebes

SINGAPORE

INDONESIA

Java

EAST TIMOR

Asian animals

182	Ural owl
183	Pelican
184	Jerboa
185	Fennec fox
186	Jellyfish
187	Soldier fish
188	Snappers
189	Reindeer
190	Kestrel
191	Snow leopard
192	Bengal tiger
193	Indian elephant
194	Sea anemones
195	Tiger shark
196	Bactrian camel
197	Giant panda
198	Polar bear
199	Siberian tiger
200	Wolf
201	Mongolian ass
202	Chinese water deer
203	Sun bear
204	Orangutan
205	Walrus
206	Fur seal
207	Japanese crane
208	Puffer fish
209	Seahorse
210	Proboscis monkey

The numbers in the key are on the stickers.

Animal records

There are all kinds of amazing animals living around the world. On these pages you can find out about some of the most spectacular, record-breaking animals, including the biggest, smallest and rarest creatures alive today.

Biggest

■ **Mammals** – A fully-grown blue whale weighs more than 20 elephants.

■ **Birds** – Ostriches can be as tall as 2.7m (9ft). An ostrich egg is about the size of a basketball and would make an omelette big enough to feed about 20 people.

■ **Land animals** – African elephants grow up to 3.7m (12ft) tall. Even newly-born elephants are 1m (3ft) tall.

Smallest

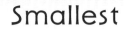

■ **Insects** – The world's smallest insect is a kind of wasp, called a fairyfly, that grows to only 0.14mm (0.006in) long.

■ **Birds** – Cuban bee hummingbirds are only 56mm (2in) long – about the size of your thumb.

■ **Reptiles** – Dwarf geckos, from the Dominican Republic, are 16mm (0.6in) long.

African elephants have thick, wrinkled skin, which protects them from the baking sun in Africa.

Chihuahuas and other very small dogs are known as "toy dogs".

Small blue macaws live in the rainforests of Brazil.

Three-toed sloths look slightly green because they move so slowly that mossy plants grow on their fur.

Rarest

■ **Birds** – Small blue macaws are the rarest birds in the world. Only one male still lives in the wild today.

■ **Rhinoceroses** – There are only around 60 Javan rhinoceroses living wild in Indonesia, in southeast Asia.

■ **Dolphins** – Baiji river dolphins are only found in the Yangtze river, in China. Many have died because of pollution and fishing in the river, and there are fewer than 150 left.

Fastest

■ **Fliers** – Peregrine falcons can fly as fast as 180kph (112mph) and can travel long distances to find a place to nest.

■ **Swimmers** – Sail fish can reach speeds of up to 110kph (68mph).

■ **Runners** – Over short distances, cheetahs can run at 105kph (65mph) – that's about the same speed as a fast car.

Slowest

■ **Mammals** – Three-toed sloths move at 2m (6ft) a minute. They also spend most of their time fast asleep, not getting anywhere.

■ **Water animals** – Sea anemones move so slowly that if you watched one, it wouldn't seem to move at all.

■ **Non-movers** – Some animals, such as barnacles, sponges and corals, don't move. They grow fixed to rocks or the sea bed.

Cheetahs' powerful, sleek bodies enable them to run at record-breaking speeds.

Index and checklist

This checklist will help you to find every animal in the book. The first number after each entry tells you which page it is on. The second number (in brackets) is the number on the sticker.

Picture researcher: Ruth King
Cover designer: Stephen Moncrief
Digital manipulation: Mike Olley, Emma Julings and John Russell